The Belan Deck

Matt Bucher

Sideshow Media Group Press

Los Angeles / Austin

Sideshow Media Group Press
Los Angeles / Austin
SideshowMediaGroup.com

10 9 8 7 6 5 4 3 2

I am standing at the corner of Folsom and Embarcadero waiting for an Uber.

I can see the cars on the Bay Bridge frozen, stationary.

No MUNI trains are barreling down the Embarcadero at this time of day.

Beyond a few palm trees outlined in the aquamarine sky, just below the descending clouds, I can see the top of the arrow of Claes Oldenburg's *Cupid's Span*.

There is the breeze and the smell that seemingly never leaves San Francisco.

Fifty-eight degrees.

I have the Uber app open, SFO as destination but have not yet hit *Confirm*.

I glance at thc Teslas and SUVs in the intersection, glance back at my phone again.

There are several cars stopped on the Embarcadero, almost all Uber and Lyft drivers I'm certain.

Once I tap *Confirm* I know my ride will be accepted in seconds and I will get into one of these cars.

Just then I had an incoming call: Jimmy Chen.

I hate incoming calls and the immediate panic they induce.

Breathe in. Accept.

Hey Jimmy, I'm on my way to the airport right now. Gotta get back to Austin tonight. Can we talk later?

No, no, it's fine. Totally understand. Just thought I'd give you a heads up that the meeting I mentioned, the one with the Board, that's actually happening on Monday now and I just wanted, I mean, wanted to call you.

I can barely focus on what he's saying. The traffic is muffling all other sounds and I need to get into this Uber right now.

I squint at a black sedan. The driver saw me looking at my phone.

Jimmy, is this regarding the issue of my ongoing employment?

That's on the agenda. I mean, yeah, but I mean, I just wanted to give you a heads up. So I'll need that deck on Sunday. The one for Belan.

A tech bro wearing a hoodie and a gray backpack shoots past me on a skateboard. A mother with a stroller maneuvers around me.

Can we talk about this later, please? I'm obstructing pedestrians and I'm on my way to the airport.

Yeah, yeah of course. Just wanted to give you a heads up. But I need that deck sooner rather than later, OK? Sunday morning if you don't mind.

Got it.

End.

Tap Uber. *Confirm.*

Your driver is now arriving. Black Mercedes S580. License plate PEV4391.

The Embarcadero morphs into the 101 and

soon we are stuck in the usual parking lot traffic. I don't mind. I have an hour or three to spare.

I like to get to the airport early.

I don't like to entertain the idea of being late.

Maybe that's an understatement.

And, despite some awful experiences in the past, I don't mind SFO.

It feels familiar. An old friend.

And I don't think of myself as a typical business traveler. Whatever that means.

Weathered men, pale in drab suits, or, more likely now, in Salesforce-logoed Patagonia vests and quarter-zips, always on their laptops, racking up millions of miles, discussing sports or crypto.

That ain't me.

Most of the time, at the airport, I can't bring myself to do that sort of work anyway.

Physically, mentally, I don't find the space conducive to office work.

I am a traveler. Even while commuting.

My preference is for a paper book, a pencil or pen, a paper notebook to write in, a restaurant or bar where I can watch the never-ending flow of humanity, then to go browse the shops, read some more.

Do nothing, in a way. For once.

I always have several paper journals on me at all times, especially when I travel.

Claes Oldenburg died of complications from a fall.

Falls are the leading cause of injury-related death among adults age 65 and older.

Belan is the Chairman and CEO. When I first met him, after I'd been hired and flown to San Francisco, I was shocked when I saw his name.

My great-grandfather had been named Belan when he was born, but had been adopted later at the age of 21 and he changed his name.

We call him Leo Steven. But I never met him.

When I met this Belan, the CEO, this was the first thing I told him.

Belan was a family name. On my dad's side.

Just as I started to launch into the story, he cut me off: Interesting. Huh. Well, about this strategy deck you're working on…

I'd never met another person named Belan

in my life, and I doubt he had either but that apparently didn't matter to him at all. He was all business, all the time. I could feel the stress emanating off him like steam.

I made it through the precheck line, no bags to check, and headed toward gate B39.

My phone vibrated. It was Amanda. She wasn't my assistant, exactly. But she "supported" everyone on the team by doing things like booking travel and ordering office supplies and scheduling meetings.

Flight delayed 2 hours. Go to gate C42.

Thanks, I text back. Then I text my wife: Flight delayed, don't wait up.

Belan had a few weird rules, like insisting no one use the word "I" in any memos or decks. Meetings must start at 10 minutes past the hour. No ties.

Jimmy told me: crack a golf joke to get on his good side, loosen him up. He loves the Kentucky Derby.

Incredibly, SFO has a bargain book store. Or at least I have never seen another airport bookstore with a large bargain section. And one stocked with many small-press books. I headed there before leaving B terminal.

One thing I spent too much time worrying about was the title of the PowerPoint deck.

Naming things can feel impossible, but when it's done well, it's as if that thing could never be called something else.

I tried to take inspiration from titles of poems.

I'd browse anything vaguely literary, looking for phrases that stood out as titles. Found poems.

Desperate for a good title.

Dave Winer has a whole manifesto about not sweating the name of something, i.e. software. Of course a software developer would just say "foo" and move on.

This deck for Belan would be the biggest deck of my life. It would have to be. And not just the number of slides. Metaphorically it would make or break my career.

Jimmy made sure I knew my job was on the line.

Read between the lines.

The deck would be my best and final offer, my ultimate attempt to articulate it all.

And there were dozens of slides illustrating a vision and framework for the future roadmap of our AI/ML product lines.

And so I worried over the name of it, what

should go on slide #1, in the filename Jimmy would see in the attachment and in the subject line of the email.

It had to be perfect.

I kept a running list of possible titles in my Field Notes notebook, the one I keep in my pocket.

> Thought: A Moral Tale
>
> Digital Transformation Strategy for AI/IT & Machine Learning Solutions and Services FINAL
>
> *Truth and Beauty in Crisis*
>
> Why Humans Read and Love

None of these were right. But I kept trying them out on slide #1, changing the font and background.

> Evolution of Thought as it Relates to Humans
>
> My Own Tripartite Journey
>
> The Odyssey of AI Through the Ages

AI AI AI. I have AI on the brain because of this stupid job.

AI Ai Wei Wei.

Ai is also a three-toed sloth.

I learned that in first grade because I read the dictionary starting at A.

The deck is a utilitarian format. It's not meant for art or literature.

Edward Tufte claimed that PowerPoint "routinely disrupts, dominates, and trivializes content" and much worse.

We trivialize virtually everything meaningful to humans in a market economy.

Life is transmuted into trivia, bullets, rows.

That not technically blood-related great-grand-father I mentioned that day was born Leo Steven Belan in Berlin, Germany, on November 17, 1890, to Paul and Elizabeth Belan.

Nonlinear, discontinuous. Maybe more of a collagelike letter than a deck.

Cut and pasted, right click, Add New Slide.

If you don't play around with the form, you're not meant to be taken seriously.

Leo Steven was adopted, in Powersville, Missouri, when he was 21.

1911. William Howard Taft was President.

Why would anyone adopt a 21-year-old? Is that even possible? Man adopts man.

The moving sidewalks of SFO seem old–as if they were installed when the technology was still being sorted out. Rather than a smooth, gliding motion, these belts of rubber move just a tad too fast.

And there is a springiness to the surface of the walkway that propels one's shoes both upward and forward—what you'd think the surface of the moon might be like, or perhaps not that little gravity but some intermediary planet between here and there with ground like a sponge cake.

The best spot to read in SFO, or to do anything really, is Yankee Pier. I've never been to SFO without spending time at Yankee Pier.

On May 1, 1890, the citizens of Berlin celebrated the first May Day festival in Germany. It was a workers' movement, which was responsible for voting in Social Democrats in the Reichstag elections.

Otto von Bismarck had outlawed the Social Democrat Party in 1878 for its pro-revolution, anti-monarchy ideas, but it was legalized again in 1890 and quickly swept to power.

It's not known if Paul and Elizabeth Belan were concerned about a possible revolution—surely they were workers themselves—or if they felt politically repressed by Bismarck's conservative coalition, or if they had friends emigrating to the US, or they just wanted a chance at a better life.

But for whatever reasons, my branch of the Belan family left Germany at the start of the new century.

1900 or 1901, I'm still not entirely sure of the date of their arrival at Ellis Island.

Michael Josselson was born in Estonia in 1908. His family fled *to* Germany after the Bolshevik revolution of 1917.

More titles:

> Lexemic Lush Landscape

Marks on a Street in Rome

The Berlin of the Mind

Our Own Yellow Brick Road

Why_You_Should_Hate_AI_FINAL_v2

The deck is such a mixture of content and styles that I fear no one title will be able to capture it.

My plan for the deck is to use it as a sort of intellectual grenade on the way out the door.

I am certain Belan wants to get rid of me anyway.

Art arises out of suffering. But not all suffering leads to art. Data does not suffer.

Mark Rothko, after accepting a $35,000 commission to provide paintings at the Four Seasons: "I hope to ruin the appetite of every son of a bitch who ever eats in that room."

Yankee Pier slowly fills to the point where there is a line to get in. I can't focus on anything but the deck.

Everything that is the case.

The Ravages of Time. That's what I was told once, in a nursing home.

For the individual, time may speed up or slow down, whereas, for science, it would remain the same.

I make it to gate C42 but the screen says this is a flight to Denver. I text Amanda: sure this is the right gate? Yes, she replies immediately. You've been rebooked with a 50 min layover in Denver.

Drop by my bag at the nearest attached-chair, pull out my Field Notes, and try to capture some more of these titles. Maybe more sections in the deck itself. Ambiguity Over Didacticism. Slide 1.

Who even *reads* a PowerPoint deck?

Choose Your Own Direction.

Leo Steven was 11 years old in December of 1901, and it's thought that his parents put him in the care of some other friends and family members on an advance ship to Ellis Island.

The plan was for him to meet up with his parents and siblings in Chicago.

After several adventures in New York, including a stint as a messenger boy for Broadway theaters, Leo somehow did eventually make his way to Chicago and was reunited with his parents and siblings. His mother had another child, Ann, while living in Chicago in 1906.

I'm not sure when or how Leo learned to speak English. It must've been a greater challenge for his parents.

After the Nazis came to power, Michael Josselson fled Germany and emigrated to the United States, too, working for Gimbel's department store.

Josselson? The ravages of a time forgotten.

Another title: The Internal Maze of Inhumanity

Sometime between 1907 and 1909, when he was 17 to 19 years old, Leo S. Belan left Chicago, hopped on a freight train to explore America.

Why? There is a family legend, of course.

He and a friend rode the rails to Ft. Worth, back up to Missouri, wherein he got terribly sick and stumbled off the moving train near the tiny town of Powersville.

The actuality of these events is the core of his life story; much of it remains a total mystery.

In Powersville, Leo Steven Belan was adopted, at the age of 21, by Reuben T. and Alice A. Bucher, a childless couple. Or, at least, no surviving children.

Bucher & Son.

PowerPoint was created by Robert Gaskins—a man who was an expert on the history of the English concertina.

Gaskins and his partner Dennis Austin created the software at the company Forethought, which Microsoft purchased for $14 million.

Forethought. A name I thought was original when I named a product.

Do you ever feel like you walk in a room, and you don't know why, but you're just so uncomfortable you're crawling out of your skin, even though nobody's touched you, physically? That's in *Concertina*, when you feel like you haven't excavated enough of your different personalities that when one pops up, you're not sure where it came from, and you try to hack it out of yourself. It shocks you that you could have this kind of fault, or that other people could bring it out in you.

Said Tori Amos.

Maybe I should just print out the deck when I get home. It will take hours but I can't stand working on the screen any longer.

I know that when I get home, home will be the same. But something in my mind will have changed.

The deck is a generic form, almost wholly unremarkable.

I'm not certain I could recall the details of any of the thousands of decks I've seen. This deck for Belan cannot, by definition, be great.

No deck can be great. It's antithetical to the form, which was designed to be mediocre, workaday.

And yet we don't think of novels as Word documents or really as "documents" at all. They somehow transcend all that, even the mediocre ones, and so that's what I'm attempting to do with this deck: move beyond something.

James Michener published a novel called *The Novel*.

The Deck.

Before I did a trademark search, I had named our AI product Forethought. Unaware of Gaskins and all the other products and companies who had used the mark. I thought it would be dilute. Or original.

There is some decent art on exhibit at SFO, if you can find it.

I start to text Amanda back: 'where is my new boarding pass' when I get an alert in my United

Airlines app with the new boarding pass.

An AI assistant, an algorithm at work.

While browsing Google Street View one day I saw a shop in Oslo called OLD MAPS.

Most of the writing, the actual sentences or bullets or fragments on slides: unremarkable.

Most of the books published every year: unremarkable.

Trying to find meaning through work: unenlightened, a fool's errand.

I do believe a bulleted list can be art, poetry.

Even the most sentient computer cannot "feel" the mindless pleasure of going down a deep Wikipedia rabbit hole.

Between San Francisco and Denver, looking down 30,000 feet, what's notable is the lack of human presence.

Humans can't seem to dominate nature at all from this distance. It's not until we begin to descend that roads, cars, and billboards come into view, the wormlike patterns of master-planned (yet transitory) communities unfolding.

Are those people down there really people? Teju Cole asked.

Considering that I could turn in another unremarkable deck, babble through the presentation, and move on.

But no, this time I must overturn the tables. Metaphorically.

Will Belan remember me? Does he even think I am a human being, equal to him?

AI is not improving our lives. Technology is not helping us work less or pursue more creative lives.

What would you do if you didn't have to work? Belan would never ask this.

Belan doesn't care about anything except some numbers on a screen.

He's more of a robot than the computational algorithms he owns.

I have my great-grandfather Leo Steven Belan's diaries from Powersville, Missouri. A sample week, from June 1910:

> Sunday, June 5, 1910 - Clear, warm. Attended S.S. [Sunday School] Meeting & Children's Exercises at Christian Church [*reminding myself that Leo Steven was a native German speaker*]

> Monday, June 6, 1910 - Clear. Worked on shop. Tore it down.

Tuesday, June 7, 1910 - Cloudy most of day. Worked on shop.

Wednesday, June 8, 1910 - Cloudy all day, rained P.M. Worked for A. Cozad [*a neighbor*]

Thursday, June 9, 1910 - Cloudy all day, rained P.M. Worked for F.G.C. 9h.

Friday, June 10, 1910 - Clear. Worked for F.G.C.

Saturday, June 11, 1910 - Worked for A. Cozad

Sunday, June 12, 1910 - Clear warm. Drowned two horses (Black) (One Horse & one mare) Drove in pond to wash wheels, horse laid down and pulled mare over him, got tangled in harness.

This horse-drowning incident was one of the few family myths passed down to us over the past century.

Though the details were often confused, the general idea was that this was a life-altering event.

A modern-day equivalent might be totaling one's vehicles with the crash destroying a laptop, phone, desktop, modem, and all means of supporting one's self instantly gone—yet existentially worse because the horse was a living animal and not a machine.

Thomas Merton accidentally electrocuted himself on a portable Hitachi fan in Thailand.

Frank Pasquale warned of the dangers of mechanistic mimicry, when AI attempts to simulate humanity.

The first SFMOMA mini-exhibit can be found between terminals B and C. It's all black and white photographs this time, each maybe three feet tall by five feet wide.

The first photograph in the series is of a woman in what looks like 1920s clothes, maybe earlier. She stares directly at the camera.

And of course what's striking about this photo,

why it's on exhibit here, is that the woman seems modern. She appears to be from our era, stuck back then.

What did people make of her then? No doubt she was completely oppressed by the gender expectations of her time.

How did her photo end up here? She has high-cheek bones and a sly grin, her hair is down. I can't find a card on the wall that gives her name or the photographer's name.

What remains of a person after they're gone? When someone switches jobs and you never see them again, what sort of impact is really left behind?

It's all transitory.

None of it matters.

Has any PowerPoint deck ever made a lasting

impact on anyone ever? Perhaps. A book?

What remains in you once you have read it?

We all hate unanswered questions in PowerPoint decks.

I take out my Field Notes and write "No questions in Deck. Ever."

One title: *Survival mode in AI Experience Management*.

AI has no inherent interest in anything except being programmed to do a task.

AI has no use-case for a Wikipedia rabbit hole. Why click another link?

I look at the next black and white photo in the series. It's an old man named Mills.

He does not look modern.

A human being has the capacity to suddenly find a topic interesting and follow it indefinitely.

An epiphany cannot exist artificially.

AI can randomize topics or data, it can infer from sets of commands, but this is at the heart of what separates humans from machines. Computers cannot yet effectively reproduce human curiosity, creativity, motivation, or emotions.

This old man Mills looks like a photo I saw of a dust bowl farmer once. Except Mills is wearing a suit and tie and not overalls. They both had this blankness to their eyes, ragged cheeks and brow.

The next photo is of a man at a racetrack standing next to a horse.

A jockey sits on the horse and the two men appear happy, as if they–meaning the horse– have just won the race.

Computers were invented by mathematicians and scientists in order to solve mathematics problems.

Computers have only improved typing and writing marginally.

Steve Jobs was not an artist.

Capitalism is incompatible with being an artist, for most people.

A chicken is only the method an egg uses to make another egg.

A card on the wall says the title of the photo is Oakvine Woods Win.

Nom de course is a racing name.

If you are a rich asshole with dozens of thoroughbreds in a Kentucky barn somewhere, you don't simply call it "Belan's Stables."

That will not do.

You need a *nom de course* such as Golden Eagle Barn or Oakvine Woods or Newfields Country Stables or some other bullshit pseudonym you use for your LLC.

Ogden Mills, the card says.

We are biased against clear writing. We believe that denser, more opaque writing must somehow be smarter, better.

Machines do not have this bias. Clear text is easier to parse.

Olan Mills.

Why is it so hard to name things?

Seabiscuit was bred and owned by Wheatley Stable, the *nom de course* of Ogden Mills and his sister Gladys.

Ogden Mills himself was one of the causes of the dust bowl and the Great Depression.

As Hoover's Treasury Secretary, Mills pushed for higher taxes, spending cuts, and opposed all of the New Deal reforms Roosevelt wanted.

Belan won't care.

Though he lived in New York, Mills inherited a large plot of land, a pasture, just south of San Francisco.

The 150-acre cow pasture was originally purchased by his grandfather, Darius Ogden Mills, who was, for a time, the richest man in California.

Eventually, we are all forgotten.

Millbrae, California, was named after Darius Ogden Mills.

In 1927, the city of San Francisco leased that cow pasture from the Mills family for the purposes of building an airport, originally called Mills Field.

Ogden Mills died of a sudden heart attack at age 53.

No amount of money or high office can save you.

Your obituary might be on the front page of the *New York Times*, as Mills' was.

But you will be forgotten.

They might name a city and an airport after you. Ninety years later, at most, totally forgotten.

This is freedom.

Passengers enplaned and deplaned at SFO fell

71% during 2020, thanks to the pandemic.

The closest it's been to a cow pasture since 1927.

I know no one will read the deck or forward it or save it to their desktop or remember it at all.

They will laugh it off and the idea of the deck will leave their minds in a matter of hours or minutes.

And yet I cannot stop making the deck.

"... but the dust of time falls on everything that has been written and so I think it's right if every ten years someone else draws a line through all those old things and describes the world-of-today in different words."
—Louis Paul Boon, *Chapel Road*

Jim Whittaker was the first employee of REI and the first American to summit Mount

Everest.

Belan, the CEO, is a short person. He sports the type of goatee you'd see in popular representations of the three musketeers.

New title: *My Soul Expanding.*

A Soul Expands.

Soulquake.

There is a book out there, being written today, that is just for you.

Two older Asian women in sun hats and masks and sunglasses are using trekking poles as they walk laps around the inner perimeter of Terminal C.

A skinny, white-haired distinguished gentleman in a paisley polo is carrying a mesh shoulder bag containing a white Pomeranian.

A round-faced, red-eyed man wearing a Texas Longhorns ballcap mouths the word "morning" to me as he passes by.

Where does time go?

Sit and wait.

A year after JFK's assassination, Canada named a 14,000-foot peak in Kluane National Park after him: Mount Kennedy. It had never been climbed.

The first to ascend to the summit of Mount Kennedy was Robert F. Kennedy. The expedition was led by Jim Whittaker.

I had to catch a flight. An attempt to return home. Otherwise marooned in Mills' Field.

All the men from that first expedition in 1965 are now dead, except for Jim Whittaker.

Is this old man across from me here in Terminal C, in his REI windbreaker and Merrell hiking boots, just another retiree tourist in SF or is it Jim Whittaker?

FORMER SECRETARY OF TREASURY IS STRICKEN BY HEART ATTACK IN HIS HOME HERE.

Check the phone: I need to get back to Austin. Ask Amanda to find another flight?

New title: *Marks on the Street*.

Marketing as gift.

Marketing as unrequited love.

Machine learning implies that we will be able to teach machines to take all the crappy jobs.

Marks on a screen. Pixels on a page in Rome.

How can a distracted generation surrounded by screens of flashing lights be expected to read or write anything?

Otto von Bismarck. @OttoVanBismarck.

I can't fail this time. I won't fail. It's not in me.

The True Deck For Belan, or The Way Consciousness Works.

AI can't kill anything worth preserving.

Art as redemption for computers.

My desperate voice has become my only way out.

The ethics of machine learning imply machines built by flawed humans.

But one day humans will succeed in making

humans irrelevant.

On some of these business trips I get an inexplicable, desperate urge, a longing, to return home as quickly as possible.

Other days I linger.

Writer Vernor Vinge predicted the singularity would occur between 2005 and 2030.

The more we learn about animal behavior and intelligence, the more we learn humans aren't so unique.

A 2012-2013 poll of scientists suggested a median probability estimate of 50% that artificial general intelligence would be developed by 2040 or 2050.

The casual promise of a future nightmare.

Every line in my journals could now be used as

a title for the deck.

We all want the unknowable, the sublime.

The journals, the deck, the experience of waiting, the return home—it will all merge into one superintelligent singularity.

The dominant ethos of our times: who cares as long as my side wins.

Richard Linklater kept a picture of Edward Albee above his writing desk.

A computer doesn't need to discover who it is. There is no inspiration, no "who" to begin with.

Intelligence is one thing, but empathy is quite another.

Give me artificial creativity—is there such a thing? Kenneth Goldsmith?

Of course "intelligence" is used as a synonym for spying, too.

Of course AI meaning Allen Iverson.

This convenient modifier encompasses one of the 22 primary rabbit holes that serve as the early foundations of Section 2 in the deck for Belan.

The human motivation behind a work of art requires more than knowledge or understanding to influence the receiver.

One of the first things Belan told me at our weekly planning meeting is that he didn't want to see any more data models: no more inputting random trivia (my specialty) or data at all. No more wiki data or spreadsheets.

Neural networks had advanced past that point in the late nineties.

My counterpoint to him: not really.

Human inferences between facts, between coincidences, circumstances, unwritten rules, nuances, memories–all of this could be learned by algorithms, Belan argued.

Prove it.

Meetings have a very low rate of information transfer.

New title: *What it Means to Be Human–or Inhuman.*

How to frame it as a manifesto disguised as a non-manifesto.

"Human," as a noun, dates only from the 1530s. Its Old English equivalent was "guma," a word you can sort of still see in "bridegroom."

Insert new slide, copy and paste.

Intelligence as the Quality of Sagacity and Comprehending General Truths

1. It was reported that James Joyce's grandson (and literary executor), Stephen, has in his home only three feet or so of shelf space devoted to his grandfather's books.

2. While at Harvard, Stephen Joyce roomed with Henri Matisse's grandson, Paul, and Sadruddin Aga Khan, who helped fund several of his expat friends who wanted to start a literary journal called *The Paris Review*.

3. Prince Sadruddin and George Plimpton had worked together on the *Harvard Lampoon*.

4. If ever there was a man born for the *Lampoon* (of the 1950s, of ever), it was John Updike.

5. Updike's work on the *Harvard Lampoon* overlapped with the editorship of Fred Gwynne, who went on to play Herman Munster.

6. Prince Sadruddin's foundation was itself funded, we know now, by the C.I.A. Plimpton himself worked as an "agent of influence" for the CIA. Another *Paris Review* founder, Peter Matthiessen, was a CIA operative at

the time, using his literary work as a cover for postwar espionage and propaganda.

7. (A friend of David Foster Wallace's suggested that Wallace picked up the usage of annular circle symbols in *Infinite Jest* from Matthiessen's use of sun signs in *Far Tortuga*.)

8. Another *Paris Review* co-founder, Thomas Guinzberg, was the son of the founder of Viking Press. Thomas became president of Viking when his father died in 1961. He famously hired Jacqueline Kennedy Onassis to be an editor in 1975.

9. John Updike was asked to sit for a *Paris Review* interview in 1966 and refused, citing his (pretty obviously disingenuous) lack of substantive answers for interviewers in general. He reluctantly accepted in 1967 and was interviewed by celebrity-profiler Charles Samuels.

10. At the height of the Cold War, Samuels co-wrote a book with FBI double agent Boris Morros called *My Ten Years as a Counterspy*, which was made into a movie starring Ernest Borgnine.

11. Updike's roommate at Harvard was

Christopher Lasch, who wrote *The Culture of Narcissism* and *The New Radicalism in America*.

12. In 1967, while Updike was being interviewed by the *Paris Review*, Lasch wrote an article for *The Nation* revealing that the *Paris Review*, and dozens of other literary magazines, were funded by a CIA front organization called the Congress for Cultural Freedom.

13. Try to imagine if, fifty years from now, it was revealed that Buzzfeed or *McSweeneys* or *n+1* or any other mainstream "literary" magazine was, in fact, funded by a secret C.I.A. program.

14. Fortunately, anti-communism—as a literary goal—managed to merely graze the aesthetic and fictional endeavors it supported. As far as we know.

15. Another founder of the *Paris Review* is almost completely forgotten: H.L "Doc" Humes.

16. H.L. Humes left an unfinished novel about a scientist named Dorsey Slade, described as "science fiction about a character who becomes another character,

and about a writer going mad." In 2007, Humes' daughter said she would try to complete the novel herself. It remains unfinished.

17. Humes published one unabashed masterpiece of expatriate literature: *The Underground City*.

18. Max Aub was responsible for placing Picasso's Guernica at the 1937 International Exposition.

19. Aub also wrote for the CCF-CIA-funded Mexican literary journal *Mundo Nuevo*.

20. Almost every poet and writer published in a literary journal in postwar Europe was in some way tied to the CCF, though few of them knew of any real connection to the CIA.

21. The CCF funded *Encounter*, which was edited by Irving Kristol and Stephen Spender, who was soon replaced by Melvin J. Lasky.

22. Lasky also edited *The Anchor Review*, founded by Anchor Books and Jason Epstein as a sort of trade-paperback sized literary review. Its second issue contained the first

excerpt of Nabokov's *Lolita* published in the U.S.

23. *The Anchor Review* #2 featured a (frankly unimpressive) cover design by Milton Glaser and typography by Edward Gorey.

24. Gorey also collaborated with John Updike on a short book called *The Twelve Terrors of Christmas*. One of the terrors is the concept of Santa Claus.

25. The people behind the people behind the front organizations who advocated for spending US. Government dollars on the creation and production of literary magazines sincerely believed that "cultural achievement and political freedom were interdependent."

26. Are those who believe in that mission today willing to go so far as to accept C.I.A. funding to prove its viability?

Discovering "truths" (his term), actively searching for new routes of perception, rather than relying on another human to feed them: the future of computing, Belan argued.

The argument that truth-seeking relies, in large part perhaps, on serendipity.

Horace Walpole coined the word serendipity in a 1754 letter to Horace Mann. Walpole claimed to have taken it from the Persian fairy tale "The Three Princes of Serendip," whose heroes were "always making discoveries, by accidents and sagacity, of things they were not in quest of."

Serendip being an old name for Ceylon, which is the old name for Sri Lanka.

Attempting to construct a mini-world or a simulacrum in which another person can make discoveries of truth by accident, in a deck.

Clues rather than trivia.

An item in the May 15, 1918 Unionville Republican: "(Crowded out last week.) Leo S. Bucher left Monday for St. Louis to enlist in the navy."

The picture of a computer browsing the internet it created: any understanding of the human intention behind each webpage?

Solving problems indirectly, using reasoning that is not immediately obvious, is often considered paranormal or pseudoscience by these science-only types.

I showed Belan an early draft of the deck, maybe 90 slides, and he said "it's trying to get at something important, but it's not there. I don't like all these little bits of unconnected trivia."

So I added 454 more slides.

It's not a deck. What are you trying to say?

I thought it was obvious.

AI is incapable of aiming at beauty, much less the sublime.

Science may accidentally reveal beauty, but software itself is almost entirely devoid of beauty.

Code, like mathematics, has the potential for elegance. But it's beauty we want and the sublime we need.

Belan secretly can't wait for the singularity to occur–to watch in awe as humans are enslaved and eventually exterminated by sentient, caring robots.

All Watched Over by Machines of Loving Grace.

Serendipity is crucial because it expands your horizons. You need that if you want to be free. Said Cass Sunstein.

Waiting for the penny to drop.

People who hate facts and trivia in novels.

In books.

In life.

Show me where the trivia hurt you.

Books are made out of books.

The Wikipedia rabbit hole as art, as immersive escapism.

You can scroll through the deck, all 500 slides, in about 12 seconds. No one will.

Flip the pages.

Not for me, Belan said.

Repetition as change.

What's at stake? Jimmy had asked.

Taste is foundational to rhetoric. Said Hugh Blair.

The Thoughts Behind Thoughts.

My taste dooms me.

The domain of art, whatever the subject may be.

Belan wants something more linear. Just make it more straightforward.

We have to tell a story here.

The right words in the right order.

A *récit*.

How to Feel Productive and Useful.

Gnomic suggestions.

Do the dishes. Weed the garden. Active meditation, monklike.

Did anyone tell Richard Hamilton to make it more linear?

Hannah Höch: just give us something straightforward.

No need for the scissors.

William Gass grew up in a town without a bookstore.

In 1942 FDR said that if he could start life over he'd probably go into advertising.

If you are making anything completely linear, it's probably too simple.

Unpopular opinion: Pearl S. Buck deserved the Nobel Prize, and schools should continue to teach and promote *The Good Earth*.

One more filled notebook, check the phone's lockscreen.

Not much interest in exposition, obviously.

Everything's at stake.

July 1944: FDR accepts nomination to a fourth term; Saint-Expury disappears; George Plimpton arrives at Harvard; a circus tent in Hartford, Connecticut, catches fire, killing 167 people.

June 1965: Johnny Cash's truck catches fire in a California forest, burning down 500 acres, nearly wiping out the nesting territory of the California condor.

When we buy a book, we think we are buying time to read.

From the lengthy obituary of Leo Steven's adopted father: "Considerable time is given to the writing of this man's life work for he deserves it—and as time passes his friends will fully appreciate the fact that it was better this man passed this way."

New title, Slide 1: BLAGUES

A computer cannot produce a sunset or a redwood.

You cannot experience a sunset online.

There was an AI bingo card floating around on Twitter, courtesy of @nabla_theta.

Belan hated it.

Some of the entries were verbatim taken from Belan's interviews in *Wired* and *The Atlantic*.

"Smarter AI will also be more moral."

"Just give AI more sympathy for humans."

"We shouldn't try to obstruct the evolution of intelligence."

"We can just turn off the AI if it turns against us."

"Maybe AI killing us all won't be so bad."

Another tweeter, @robbensinger, added responses to all the entries on the bingo card.

Just penalize the Al for killing people.

"We don't know how to penalize AGI systems for an action in training, in a way that robustly ensures it won't carry out the action. And again, human values are complex and fragile."

Gravity's Rainbow was almost titled *Mindless Pleasures*.

When *Gravity's Rainbow* won the National Book Award, Thomas Guinzberg, publisher of Viking Press, suggested to Pynchon that comedian Irwin Corey should accept the award on his behalf.

The only person really thanked in Corey's rambling speech was Thomas Guinzberg.

The jury of the National Book Award divided the prize between Pynchon and Isaac Bashevis Singer (for *A Crown of Feathers and Other Stories*) that year.

Language is only necessary when communication is endangered.

Maybe keep the AI locked in servers, effectively away from the real world.

A list of street names does not describe a place.

A list of towns visited does not describe a

journey.

Language is always an abbreviation.

THE REAL EARTH.

Virtual Reality Sunset.

The sad consolation of having been "nominated" for a Nobel prize.

Nominated for a Pushcart.

Writing anything requires the writer to ignore the immediate circumstances of life, in real life, and focus on the text.

Sometimes I go about in pity for myself. All the while a great wind carries me across the sky.

No need for meta-commentary, Jimmy tried to tell me.

Too bad. The whole thing is meta-commentary.

Unattributed.

The proper work of the critic is praise, and that which cannot be praised should be surrounded with a tasteful, well-thought-out silence.

I was born, and then I liked books.

You see a name there but that's not me.

We aren't really Belans.

The Good Earth.

We're adopted. We all choose our families.

Read read read but you can't hope to retain it all. Bits and pieces remain.

The deck has always been a workshop, not a museum.

A deck where one can dip and dip out.

Hate calling it a "deck" but also hate "PowerPoint" and "Presentation."

It's not just a document.

Computers are expected to retain it all, not just fragments.

New title: *Will it Play in Peoria?*

Blagues for Belan.

The deck is not well-organized but there is a middle section of the deck.

Midway upon the journey of our life I found myself within a forest dark. For the straightforward pathway had been lost.

Corporate America has ruined the word "journey."

Do you understand what I am saying? Does it also feel this way to you?

The middle section of the deck is really an NLP experiment using Natural Language Inference (NLI) models. Inferences are among the most difficult tasks in developing intelligence, human or artificial.

What I am mostly giving the model is unlabeled, human-created resources, which Belan thinks are outmoded.

This company was founded on unsupervised learning, he used to say.

I didn't say: I don't care about your company.

The slides aren't labeled "inferences" or "matched associations" or anything. They are data points.

Nicanor Parra died the day after Ursula K. LeGuin died.

Larry McMurtry and Beverly Cleary died the same day.

Lionel and Diana Trilling were born 17 days apart.

Sean Lennon was born on John Lennon's 35th birthday.

Albert Einstein was born on Pi Day, 1879.

John Smith, John Berryman was born.

The model, the neural network itself, would need to digest all known literature, all human knowledge, before it could begin sorting.

Make sense of trivia, of coincidences, of probability.

John Ashbery and Walter Becker died on the same day.

Jean Stein committed suicide at age 83.

Edward Albee died the same day as W.P. Kinsella.

Clarice Lispector died the day before her 57th birthday.

Elvis outlived Nabokov by 45 days.

Ingmar Bergman and Michelangelo Antonioni died on the same day.

Federico Fellini and River Phoenix died on the same day.

Olivia Newton John and David McCullough died on the same day.

Evan S. Connell died the day before Aaron Swartz died.

Of course people die everyday, but Shakespeare and Cervantes on the same day, Adams and Jefferson: what are the odds?

Jean Stein's first husband worked under Robert F. Kennedy in the Justice Department.

People say "life is messy" and then want tidy stories.

Wallace Stevens' wife Elsie was the model for Liberty on the Mercury dime.

D.H. Lawrence's wife Frieda was a distant relative of the Red Baron.

Like most, I have trouble watching an hour-long TV show without wanting to look at my phone, further fragmenting the reality of the "reality" show.

Nobel laureate Louise Glück's niece played an inmate on "Orange is the New Black."

It's more than simple attention deficit: a deep need to escape from one path and pursue another rabbit hole until another escape presents itself.

Our ability to pay attention to the paths before us has never been greater.

You are tired. You are true of heart.

Right click, open in new tab.

In the Chicago production of *Hamilton*, the actor playing Alexander Hamilton is named Miguel Cervantes.

The first-ever NFL draft was held in 1936. Third overall pick, from Notre Dame: William Shakespeare.

The Merchant of Menace.

Frank Shakespeare served as ambassador to the Vatican.

Francis Shakespeare, whose parents were named Frances and Francis.

A different Frank Shakespeare won a gold medal in rowing at the 1952 Olympics.

Headline in the Unionville Republican, June 7, 1911: "T.B. CARNIVAL HERE / The Dream of The Small Boy and the Peanut Vendor Realized."

What we are teaching AI/machine learning models/NLP is outdated almost instantly. Modeling human behavior and thought is aiming at an ever-shifting target.

Data lakes, data oceans, galaxies of data ad infinitum.

There is an explicitly labeled manifesto section of the deck.

Belan's models have never tagged or labeled or self-organized sets of manifestos.

Jake Chapman said taking children to art galleries is a total waste of time since children "are not human yet."

Princess Diana's grandfather allegedly said he didn't see the point of ordinary people.

Francesca Woodman died at 22. Suicide.

The human heart is a mystery-making machine.

Zola died of carbon monoxide poisoning due to a poorly ventilated chimney.

Tom Seaver died of Covid and Lewy Body Dementia.

Bill Buckner died of Lewy Body Dementia.

Robin Williams committed suicide, but his autopsy revealed he'd suffered from Lewy Body Disease.

Buckner and Seaver played against each other in the 1986 World Series.

Buckner had also been in the outfield for Hank Aaron's 715th home run.

One of Obama's great-grandfathers was named Ralph Waldo Emerson Dunham.

Stories, as Ishiguro said, are like saying to someone "This is how it feels to me. Do you understand what I'm saying? Does it also feel this way to you?"

It's absurd to ask a computer the second question.

April 1925: *The New York Times* reports that a speaker has told the National Liberal Club that the novel is dead.

We can't all be Dickens or Dostoevsky. Or David Markson.

By necessity, by proclivity–and by delight, we all quote. Said Emerson.

N.B.: All non-standard syntax and grammar is intentional and Author respectfully requests that it be stetted.

What is happiness? It's a moment before you realize you need more happiness. Said Don Draper.

Ezra Pound told James Laughlin to become a publisher since he (Laughlin) had no talent for poetry.

Zola's remains were not moved to the Pantheon until five years after his death. During the ceremony, there was an assassination attempt on Alfred Dreyfus, who was shot but not killed.

Charles Portis was born in El Dorado, Arkansas.

Stanley Dunham, Barack Obama's grandfather, grew up in El Dorado, Kansas.

A Treatise On the Nature of Humankind.

A Failed Treatise On the Nature of Humankind.

A voice in the sky says We are now boarding for San Diego.

Clouds descending.

I received 500,000 discrete bits of information today, of which maybe 25 are important. Said David F. Wallace.

My job is to make some sense of it.

We ought really to call 'a book' only that which contains something new: the rest are only a means of learning quickly what has already been done in this or that field. Said Lichtenberg.

An attempt to smuggle reality into anything, into a PowerPoint deck.

In a newspaper database, I found this mention of Leo Steven returning to Powersville, Missouri, in 1938, after having moved to Arkansas:

> The other day I had visitors—Mr. Bucher and Mr. Young of the city of Sever Springs (Heber Springs) both former residents of Putnam county. They asked me for copies of the Old Reliable—they got 'em too. Trust they will come again

soon. Till we meet again—au revoir.

The blurring of the lines between fiction, nonfiction, work, notebooks, and exhaustion.

Of course coincidences exist and can be explained.

The characters are all fictional.

Far as I can tell, Leo was the last to really see action in a war, in our family.

Michael Jackson grew up on Jackson Street. No relation.

Unprocessed raw material, unfiltered, unsorted folders of thousands of PowerPoint files. Copy and pasted file-naming conventions.

Treat the AI like you would your child.

Raise your algorithm right and it *probably* won't try to murder anyone.

Of course humans have spent millennia developing societies and cultures that depend on mutual cooperation.

In the second century B.C., Terence said "There's nothing to say that hasn't been said before."

The dream of generations: no more war.

An Inventory of Sins.

Two data points in a data set.

Slide 1 title: The Law of Truly Large Numbers As it Applies to Data Lakes.

The large datasets of human interactions prevent us from making judgments of others' motivations.

The Unswerving Punctuality of Chance.

What do I know?

The purpose of AI is not to answer questions but to ask them.

A philosopher is someone who can sit at an airport gate for two hours and not be bored with their own thoughts.

An intelligent agent is anything which perceives its environment, takes actions autonomously, and can improve its performance through learning.

The Dream of the Small Boy.

And Belan, the peanut vendor.

I check my phone.

No more traveling for a while.

What separates humanity from animals or machines?

Our ability to create machines stands alone.

Until the machines are able to create their own machines. And kill us or enslave us.

In AI this is called the alignment problem.

How do we create benevolent intelligent machines?

Are you a farmer or a pirate? Tend to your own plot or sail the high seas?

Walt Whitman would sit on a bench at the South Street Seaport and watch waves of people come and go, swaying masses of humanity, individual points of light on each.

Our poets sit at the California Pizza Kitchen bar inside Terminal 1 at LAX, the crowds before them larger, more diverse than ever, teeming.

Wikipedia is the number one result for over 50% of all Google searches.

All airports are the same in different ways.

Wikipedia, made by humans, for free, is a better search engine than Google, the most expensive and sophisticated algorithm in the world.

Overreliance on Google sometimes occurs in determining and assessing notability for various topics and subjects on Wikipedia.

For more information about Google search limitations, see WP:GOOGLELIMITS.

New Title: Chapter 1: The Meaning of Life

at LAX.

As a child, I remember watching the terror of blue-collar Americans as their auto-factory jobs indeed were replaced by robots.

What machines cannot do well, yet: feel pain, write a memoir, secretly yearn for the boredom of the airport.

The Control Problem and Safety Engineering in Superintelligent AI.pptx.

Imagine that our universe, all space and time, is not exactly infinite but is contained in a bubble. Now imagine a sheet of bubble wrap.

Next to our universe are thousands, millions, billions, trillions, of parallel "infinite" universes in their own bubbles.

Anticonfluential.

The term "anti-novel" or "anti-roman" was first used in 1633.

The Wikipedia article for "artist" has only one photo: that of Goethe.

Seamus Heaney's last words were a text message to his wife. In Latin.

Winston Churchill's last words: I'm bored with it all.

I decide to go back to Yankee Pier to wait. There is only one table open.

We all look the same to a machine.

Levinas said "It is difficult to forgive Heidegger."

Virginia Woolf supposedly suffered from spectrophobia. The fear of mirrors.

Jennifer Egan dated Steve Jobs for a year.

The tyranny of electronic revisions means that one could work on a deck forever and never "finish" it.

We never finish reading the news.

Fugue: A dissociative state, usually caused by trauma, marked by sudden travel or wandering away from home and an inability to remember one's past.

Rabbit hole #8, starting on slide 263: Farrar, Straus and Giroux. A confluence of American ideas and personalities.

At a table facing the Y-shaped corridor of Terminal 3, the waitress is machinelike in her efficiency.

Recall that first year in San Francisco, fresh out of college, applying for jobs by reading the classifieds in the paper, going to Kinko's to fax my resume.

Later that year, a nerdy guy at work showed me a new search engine called Google.

No ads, it just worked.

I went to San Francisco then because I wished to live deliberately.

Too sincere. Too poor. Lasted only a few years.

But left with enough experience to land a string of higher-paying "comms" jobs at tech companies. So one could write in one's free time, one told oneself.

Rita Gam was married to Sidney Lumet from 1949 to 1955. After they divorced she married Thomas Guinzberg.

Lumet married Gloria Vanderbilt.

Gam and Guinzberg divorced in 1963.

Hedy Lamarr once divorced her own divorce lawyer.

Norman Vincent Peale officiated the wedding of Donald and Ivana Trump.

Rita Gam was a bridesmaid at the wedding of Grace Kelly and the Prince of Monaco.

Guinzberg fought at Iwo Jima.

Sidney Lumet spent four years as a radar repairman, stationed mostly in Burma.

Peter Gimbel served in the Army occupation force in Japan in 1946-47.

Coleridge's last words: "My mind is quite unclouded. I could even be witty."

George Eastman, inventor of the Kodak camera, suffered from a degenerative nerve disease that severely restricted his physical movement. Before he put a bullet in his heart he wrote: "To my friends: my work is done. Why wait? GE."

With Daniel Okrent, Lee Eisenberg, Peter Gethers, Harry Stein, Glen Waggoner, and Valerie Salembier, Thomas Guinzberg was a founding member of the original rotisserie baseball league.

Jack Kerouac invented several versions of fantasy baseball, and played football at Columbia.

Okrent also invented WHIP.

Okrent never won a season of rotisserie baseball.

Alexander Hamilton was never President, Okrent retorts.

Bill Buckner was one of the few major-leaguers to have played in four different decades.

Though only one game in 1969.

Dostoevsky failed entry-level algebra.

Derrida failed his entrance exams to the École Normale Supérieure. Twice.

A.E. Housman, who spent most of his adult life as a professor of Latin, failed his final exams at Oxford.

It took Durkheim three attempts to enter the ENS.

All Wikipedia articles are interconnected.

Cal Ripken, Jr., has written nearly 30 books.

The world is impossibly small.

In this life, we want nothing but facts, sir.

Paul Thomas Anderson attended film school for only two days.

Reader's Block is dedicated to Steven Moore.

Life is short, art long, opportunity fleeting, experience deceptive, judgment difficult.

It's unsatisfying. Whatever that means.

Nicholson Baker is the great-grandson of Ray Stannard Baker, Woodrow Wilson's press secretary at Versailles.

Is there anything worse than someone reading slides aloud during a meeting?

Belan once read aloud every word of a 40-slide deck, ten bullets per slide. No one commented on it.

Lucia Berlin died on her 68th birthday.

Ingrid Bergman died on her 67th birthday.

Just as we have a circadian rhythm for days, we feel an annual rhythm.

Earth below us, sky above us.

Richard Linklater once worked on an oil rig.

Carmen Maria Machado worked at LUSH in the King of Prussia mall.

John Updike's mother worked in a parachute factory.

One of Courtney Love's grandmothers was the writer Paula Fox.

Warren Commissioner Hale Boggs was the father of Cokie Roberts.

S.J. Perelman married Nathanael West's sister.

Like Hemingway, William Gaddis once lost a suitcase containing all his manuscripts.

Gaddis took it in stride, calling the loss "a touch of trouble."

When they arrested Lee Harvey Oswald in 1963, the Dallas Police Department did not own a tape recorder with which to record interviews.

Technology can't catch up. It creates holes in the timeline.

What do you want? For them to say it's great?

James Joyce struggled to earn money as a writer.

James Fucking Joyce.

Alexander Calder and Arthur Miller were neighbors.

Arthur Miller's daughter Rebecca married Daniel-Day Lewis.

Rebecca Miller's roommate at Yale: Naomi Wolf.

Wolf accused Harold Bloom of sexual harassment, or "encroachment."

Georgia O'Keefe taught public school in Amarillo, Texas.

George Saunders was born in Amarillo.

Imagine a timeline in which Zapruder was not filming that day.

To front only the essential facts of life.

Irving, Texas, longtime home of the Dallas Cowboys, is named after Washington Irving.

A play in which a painter sits down at a canvas, his back to the audience, and completes a painting start-to-finish during the course of the play. At the end, which audience member gets the painting?

Quiet but powerful baseball slugger Harmon Killebrew was once asked what his hobbies were. He replied, "Just washing the dishes, I guess."

George Clooney tried out for the Cincinnati Reds in 1977.

An encyclopedia entry demands at least a birth or a death, notability.

Early Life. Career. Death. Works. References. External Links. More than just data.

Bricolage. DIY culture. Amateurism. Fandom. Blackout poems.

All narrative art is time management. Said Kyle Beachy.

Flight leaves in an hour. I pay the bill at YP, head back to the gate. Check for any other texts from Amanda.

How AI Conquered Poker.

A computer isn't offended if you ignore it.

Does Belan lack empathy or a soul?

Rita Gam starred in a film adaptation of Sartre's *No Exit*, which was directed by Tad Danielewski, father of Mark Danielewski.

Malcolm Lowry died two weeks before Peter Gimbel.

David Belin, a lawyer for the Warren Commission, died of injuries from a fall. Belin.

Did Randall Jarrell step in front of that car or was it truly an accident?

Did Primo Levi jump or was it truly an accident?

Time hath, my lord, a wallet at his back, Wherein he puts alms for oblivion.

The computerized frustration of one's inability to fully express one's self.

An essential element of the modern rabbit hole is reading on a screen.

Change the line breaks and call it a poem.

Change one name and call it a novel.

Paste it into PowerPoint and call it a deck.

Kerouac had to change all the names in *On the Road* before it could be published.

The first draft of *The Sun Also Rises* used real names.

Just as significant is what is is not included in the deck.

PowerPoint as an outpouring of grief, a short rhetoric against the unstoppable avalanche of AI.

Self-absorption is practically a prerequisite for entrepreneurs.

There is a lot of narcissism in self-hatred. Said David Foster Wallace.

I now understand why old men are drawn to the classics, to antiquity.

Almost certain that David Markson never used

copy and paste, never saw a Wikipedia article.

I am quite content to go down to posterity as a scissors and paste man for that seems to me a harsh but not unjust description. Said James Joyce.

Yeah, right.

Gimbels went out of business mainly because they didn't keep up with the latest fashions, the latest trends. Sears, Kodak, Polaroid—one must keep up. Or else face obsolescence. The Dustbin.

It's all cumulative.

Robert Lax quit the *New Yorker* to become a clown.

Deep Blue was hailed as the first great AI chess grandmaster.

The First Great AI Philosopher after the Singularity.

Any system that can perceive its environment can also be unplugged.

Mimicking cognitive functions is not the same as learning.

Putting sentence fragments into bullets is not the same thing as writing.

I have no treasured memories related to Zoom meetings or PowerPoints shared therein.

I do have many stories and memories related to flying into San Francisco for real-world meetings.

The whole of Nature appears unnatural to our eyes. Said Chiron to Jason.

The role of "poet" can only be filled by a

human being.

I fully support the Jetsons' robots: clean the floors, do the dishes, take out the trash.

But we always know these are clearly robots in the Jetsons' home. They never created an android—a replicant that looks and acts like a human being, much less one that can mimic the conversation and emotions of a real human.

When and if Belan fires me, I won't miss him or Jimmy or any of them, really, except Dave.

Dave is the guru.

Every tech company has one, but Dave is the authentic Silicon Valley archetype.

He wears black t-shirts only, sports a thin ponytail, and mostly goes barefoot or wears sandals.

Barefoot. In a corporate office.

Dave spends months at a time in Half Moon Bay, surfing.

As far as I have seen, Dave does not have a cell phone. He's a legend, an artist with code.

He shows up for a few very important meetings every year, sans laptop.

What is the value and utility of a lifetime of reading?

Dave paces around the meeting room while others are presenting.

He occasionally offers a proverb or a pithy comment.

I'm grateful that Dave exists. Some remnant of wisdom persists.

IBM slide (1979): A computer can never be held accountable. Therefore a computer must never make a management decision.

Belan: Yes! A computer can't be held accountable so let's use the algorithm to make management decisions!

Gregor Samsa was a traveling salesman.

Thou shalt not make a machine in the likeness of a human mind. Said Frank Herbert.

Dave once told me that the generation raised by the internet is in trouble because their grasp of culture is increasingly fragmented.

The implication being that this is bad.

We pick up scraps from Wikipedia, Twitter, various links and rabbit holes, leading us to piece together lopsided images, subjective at best, of what's out there and what has been.

The best parts of the deck are copied directly from other decks.

I know Belan is paid 890 times the average employee at our company.

It's just not a deck. Said Jimmy. I don't know what it is, but it's not a real deck.

It's a jumble. It changes tenses.

It's a commonplace book.

Maybe there's something good or interesting in there, but it's buried.

I'm submitting it anyway.

A poem is just a shape.

A shape is not literature.

A deck with no plot.

A deck about nothing.

What seems beautiful to me, what I should most like to do, would be a book about nothing, a book without any exterior ties, but sustained by the internal force of its style . . . a book which would have almost no subject, or at least in which the subject would be almost invisible, if that is possible. The most beautiful works are those with least matter. Wrote Flaubert.

The deck is a way to complain about the way other people make decks.

New title: TEXT FIELDS.

New title: COMPLAINT METEOR.

New title, slide 1:
L=A=N=G=U=A=G=E, L=O=L

Has anyone ever said of a PowerPoint deck: "You could read it in one sitting"?

As a compliment?

I will begrudgingly admit that AI has made some advances in absurdity.

It's just not good, Jimmy told me.

It's not for everyone, I told him.

I change the background image on Slide 1.

The template resets.

Trying to convince some future reader to at least click through each slide.

There is a sound, a steam wand screeching primally.

The title is part of the text.

One story I'd heard about my great-grandfather Leo Steven Belan was that he'd nearly starved to death on the boat from Germany to New York. There was a man aboard the ship with a barrel of sugar and he'd let Leo Steven have a little pinch of it now and then.

Hemingway presented James Joyce with a hand-edited copy of *A Farewell to Arms*, in which he had re-inserted some of the censored text.

Interlude.

We'd heard a lot of stories.

You think your deck is more interesting than anyone else's?

Amanda texts me: new departure time 9:42pm.

I realize I have never met Amanda in person,

but I assume she is not a virtual assistant.

Some of the titles Hemingway considered for *A Farewell to Arms*: *Love in War, World Enough and Time, Every Night and All, Of Wounds and Other Causes, The Enchantment.*

Slide 1—Title: Disillusionment.

Decks do not endure.

A man in this row of seats is talking loudly on his cell phone.

My internal gauge of annoyance almost immediately peaks.

Invest in artificial intelligence without regard for intelligent ethics.

Do I have any empathy or tolerance I can summon at this moment? I must.

The man is not so different looking from me.

Older, more polished.

I shudder that this man could be, in some way, me. Future me. Alternate-reality me.

When we observe someone we are unaware of the broad range of stimuli to which they are responding.

Innovative_Data_Driven_Outcome_Focused_ Vision_and_Values_v2_MB_FINAL.pptx

Make a deck that no one else can make.

Write a bullet no one else can write.

Decks are made out of decks.

Control C, Control V, it's all too easy to add, to steal, to remix again and again.

If you are a scissors-and-paste man, where are your scraps?

The last plane out.

Nelson Algren was arrested for stealing a typewriter in Alpine, Texas.

Nabokov never delivered his promised "Anthology of Russian Poetry in English."

Barack Obama's grandmother, the woman who raised him, died two days before he was elected president.

 Salman Rushdie had dinner with Carrie Fisher the night before she died.

Studs Terkel died on Halloween, 2008—five days before Obama's election.

Specimen Days in the AI Lab.

Pencils as weapons.

The deck has been in a state of constant revision for a year. Maybe for twenty years.

Trying to think of something to text Amanda to get her to prove she is not a bot.

Maybe I should send her a CAPTCHA.

Hey Amanda, can you recommend a place to eat in SFO?

Yankee Pier, she text back immediately.

Too easy. I try again.

Anything else I should know? I ask her.

Get the popcorn shrimp! She replies.

Could be a Yelp bot. Still not sure. For now.

A wraithlike shadow passes by.

To lose ones' self. In a city, in an airport. More of a loss of time and awareness and consciousness than a loss of coordinates.

I have trouble finishing one book before starting another.

At a previous AI automation job, I found a deck so jaw-droppingly packed with incoherent HR jargon that I immediately copied it onto a flash drive.

And have used bits and pieces of that deck in writing every performance review and self-evaluation I've had to write in the past decade.

PowerPoint karaoke, or battle decks, is an improv performance where participants must deliver a presentation based on a set of slides they have never seen before.

Exhaustion at the thought of creating a persona.

Belan had created multiple personas for all our product journeys.

Melissa was a 43-year-old ad exec who listened to Terry Gross, read whatever Reese Witherspoon recommended, spent 6 to 8 minutes interacting with the GrubHub app before ordering, preferred athleisure brands that empowered women, followed 1,200+ Instagram accounts, understood the basics of CSS, and was too busy to volunteer outside of her company's Employee Resource Groups.

Andy was a 34-year-old musician and freelance web developer who biked 20 miles per week, always bought the latest iPhone via preorder, traveled overseas twice per year, collected vinyl LPs, taught himself NodeJS and ReactJS via YouTube tutorials, and expected medical websites to allow access via single-sign-on with a low latency rate.

It was all so arbitrary.

We weren't really building products for these people.

We were paying Design Thinking and Agile experts to shill their motivational wares at our staff meetings in the name of progress as defined by HR.

To speak the unspoken.

The work projects and presentations I liked best were the deeply weird ones.

The ones irrevocably intertwined with an individual's own broken soul and odd preferences.

Boarding 4 DIA in 80 minutes, Amanda texts.

Google Slides is far worse than PowerPoint and I refuse to touch it.

With everything I see in PowerPoint, I see it and read it first of all as less important, less permanent, less relevant to me, personally, because it exists in PowerPoint.

Alexander Graham Bell's last words: So little done. So much to do.

Bing Crosby's last words: Let's go have a Coca-Cola.

The pptx format is the message.

The best slides are stripped down to just a few words, or a single image or chart.

This allows the speaker to expound, explain, rather than simply read aloud.

Pecha Kucha allows the presenter 20 slides for

20 seconds each.

Human-centered Artificial Intelligence Marketing Demystified: Extracting Core Monetization Value from Scaled Customer Data through Audience Segmentation.

Show and Tell. Chit Chat. Something less than lecturing or meaningful conversations.

Show don't tell. Small talk.

Bronislaw Malinowski called it "phatic communication" in his essay "The Problem of Meaning in Primitive Languages."

The tendency to read Wikipedia articles from the bottom up.

Knut Hamsun gave the medal from his Nobel Prize to Joseph Goebbels.

For at least fifty years AI research has existed within a boom-and-bust cycle. These are boom times for funding. But Belan knows the next AI winter isn't far off.

The backlash arrives quickly. Projects get shut down.

I worry about the deck being too long or too short. Belan worries about the day VCs stop taking any calls related to AI.

It's the peculiarity of the literary man to hold forth about his own nature, to become mired in a mess of contradictions: clear-sighted and despairing, solitary yet at one with others, making fine phrases out of his bad conscience, etc. Wrote Georges Perec.

A tiredness, a wariness, with all stories, even my own.

Art, work, business, it's life that really matters. Living people. I text my wife: You still up?

I'm pacing now.

In the deck: Rabbit hole #7: Thomas Merton. Not as a biography, but as a convergence of modern thinking on the deep inner life.

Jimmy believes in training AI with synthetic data in order to eliminate biases in real data.

Yet artificial general intelligence must include the ability to reason a way out of biases.

It's more than just winning at chess.

One appeal of AI: no backstories.

Consciousness created out of circuitry. No character arcs or empathy or bathos.

In 1980, Saul Zaentz sued John Fogerty, claiming Fogerty had plagiarized his own music.

One could spend years crafting a touching, poignant, literary story about a child somewhat like oneself (poverty, trailer park, resilience, love), publish with a small-medium press, and no one care.

From the Narcissistic Personality Disorder diagnostic test: Do you find you are unwilling to recognize or identify with the feelings and needs of others?

I've now gone — and I'll admit this freely — six or seven years without a single idea for a novel. Steve Erickson told David Ulin in 2022.

Billy Joel admits he ran out of ideas for new songs in the early 1990s. No new albums since.

One idea is to create a world where every conversation you hear, every conversation you have, every conversation you imagine, adds a layer to your inner life.

The weight of it all, though.

There is no real ending. It's just the place where you stop. Said Frank Herbert.

Open my phone and turn on Do Not Disturb.

Wolfgang Paul: You probably think these ideas are crazy.

Niels Bohr: Unfortunately they are not crazy enough.

David Markson on why he did not write more novels: simple barnyard laziness.

Belan truly believes he is doing some good in the world. I hope.

There is a fierce calm.

Roaming while lost.

Take a leave from your job to roam, she'd said.

The desire to keep adding to the deck, even after I know it's done.

The serendipity of "See Also."

Art as art.

Will we live to see Congress impose bans on AI and robotics that counterfeit certain human qualities?

Gaudeamus igitur,

Iuvenes dum sumus,

Post jucundam juventutem

Post molestam senectutem

Nos habebit humus.

Deliberately Engineering Society Not to Replace Human Beings in Any Way Nor to Induce Any State of Happiness dot pptx.

Right click, delete slide. No citations needed.

There is a section about how AI should not be anonymous, hiding the identity of creators.

Frankenstein was first published anonymously, on New Year's Day 1818.

I resist the urge to look at my phone.

Robert Lax's poetic style became so stripped down in his later years that he published whole books with only a few unique words.

> black/black/black//
>
> blue/blue/blue//
>
> black/black/black/black//

Some of Lax's later work dispensed with words altogether and used only colored-squares and lines.

Author's late style: usually stripped down, bare.

The deck could always be better.
It could be smarter, Jimmy had said.

I don't disagree.

But I've learned to finish things and move on, I try to tell myself.

There is a voice, announcing.

And abruptly it's time for boarding, I realize.

I haven't been paying attention.

Time is running out, thankfully.

We are going to Denver after all.

The groups silently coalesce into rough queues.

Group 2 files past the gate agent single file,

always the one guy who doesn't have the boarding pass pulled up on his phone yet.

We bunch up inside the windowless jetway, the ripple delay of someone offscreen undoubtedly struggling with a bag too large for the overhead compartment.

I've considered it, but I've never turned around at this point.

Would they let you out of the jetway, back past the gate agent, if you faked an illness perhaps?

We shuffle forward again.

Just act like you know what you are doing.

Eventually all our graves go unattended.

Is it faking an illness if the illness is simply unseen?

Is it nonsense or brilliance? Wrote Virginia Woolf in the margin of her own manuscript.

I keep my eyes on the ground. I don't like seeing the exterior of the plane so close up.

No more "I's" in the deck. The royal "we."

Almost to the point of no return.

The flight attendant, unmasked, soulless, waiting inside.

And yet here on one shore of this wide world I stand alone, one foot planted firmly on this side of the jetway, the other stuck on the lip of that shockingly tangible aluminum fuselage of the plane, looking down at that thin strip of air and concrete below, the real earth down there somewhere underneath it all.